ULTIMATE
SPIDER-MAN
DOUBLE TROUBLE

script
BRIAN MICHAEL BENDIS

pencils
MARK BAGLEY

inks
ART THIBERT
with ERIK BENSON

colors
TRANSPARENCY DIGITAL

letters
DAVE SHARPE

associate editor
BRIAN SMITH

editor
RALPH MACCHIO

collections editor
JEFF YOUNGQUIST

assistant editor
JENNIFER GRÜNWALD

book designer
JEOF VITA

editor in chief
JOE QUESADA

publisher
DAN BUCKLEY

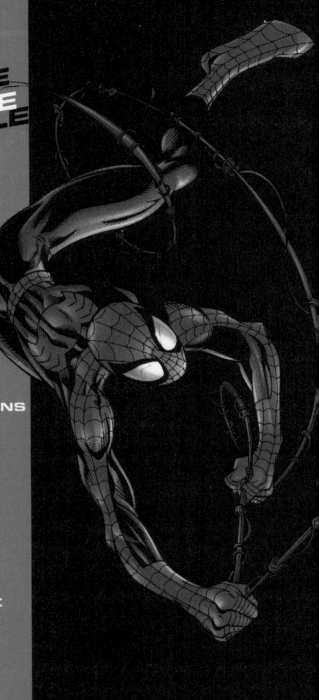

DOUBLE
DOUBLE
TROUBLE
TROUBLE

Oh my God...

We are just now beginning to understand the genetics of what has happened. There's a paper by Dr. Reed--

OH MY GOD!!!

I know this is a devastating thing to discover--

--and Doctor Lange is here to talk to you about it.

Help you through with it.

We hope the scientist in you will be able to find the exciting possibilities that this accident has brought into our lives.

We can all work together to find out what this discovery means and what maybe it holds for the future of--of--of the future.

Clifford honey, I'm going out.

Whatever.

In one week--

--you will come in here--

--and you will be a super hero.

'Do something? Keep an eye out?' Y'know what the Germans said about the Jews.

CRACK

Hey! Hey!!!

The amazing Spider-Man!!

Ladies and gentlemen, the spectacular Spider-Man!!!

How does that make him Spider-Man?

Yo! The spider bit him.

See this?

This is a frickin' bee bite I got on Saturday.

Yeah?

And I'm not Bee-Man!!

I didn't get any kind of Super Mutant Powers.

That is not--

You know what? You're nuts.

I'm telling you...

Look at him.

Look. Spider-Man is like six feet tall.

We all saw him. That is not Spider-Man.

Yeah, man, you are really being silly.

Then how do you explain those desks he broke?

He's -- A-- Spaz!

He lit the lab on fire once.

Doesn't make him the Human Torch.

That's true.

Or... does it? Ha!

Remember that--he lost his eyebrows. Ha Ha. He looked like a Star Trek Alien.

And-- and what about all of a sudden he can play basketball so good?

Dude-- He wasn't that good.

Yes, he was.

Says you.

He was.

Stacy--

--great way to start at your new school.

Second day here.

Captain Stacy?

Captain Stacy?

Captain...

Not now.

Not. Now.

I know it was you.

I just--

I can't-- --I can't even remember what we were working on at Osborn, can't remember, I--

--I went to the lab--to Osborn's labs--but they're destroyed.

But a little industrial *espionage* between friends was all right...

...so, what's a little industrial *sabotage*.

Aahh...

It--it-- it-- it hurts to--

Captain Stacy? Ben Urich from the Daily Bugle is on the line.

Tell him I passed away.

What?

Gwendolyn, I can't believe it!! I just can't.

What were you *thinking*? *Were* you thinking?

And where-oh-where did you get a *knife?*

I--

I have all these men under my command and I can't get my own daughter to do me the simple courtesy of *not* bringing a weapon to school.

What's your answer to that?

I--

Should I put you in a lockdown for a night?

Would that snap you out of this sullen little *phase* you are going through?

Because that's what they do, you know-- to little girls who pull knives on fellow students whose fathers *aren't* police captains...

They toss them in jail.

We met once before, Mr. Hammer-- at the White House.

Really?

I was there at the diplomats' dinner a couple of years ago, and you looked the President right in the eye, and you told him that the mutants were going to cost him a second term.

And I was right.

Yes, sir.

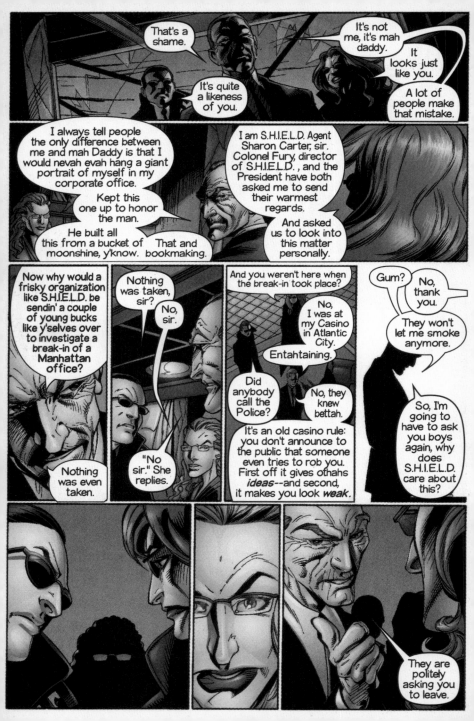

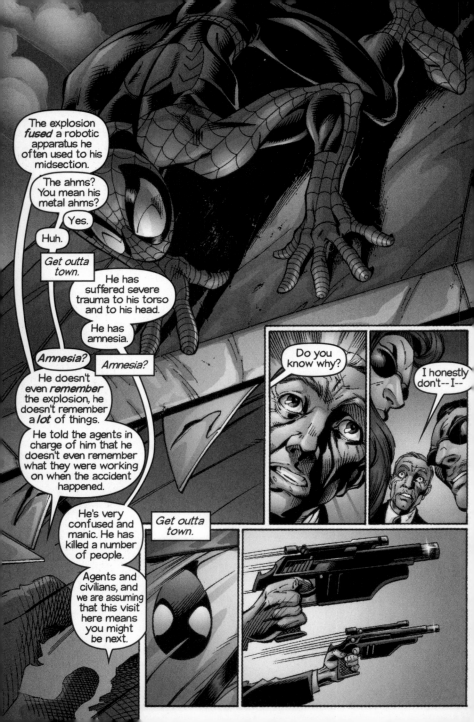

The explosion *fused* a robotic apparatus he often used to his midsection.

The ahms? You mean his metal ahms?

Yes.

Huh.

Get outta town.

He has suffered severe trauma to his torso and to his head.

He has amnesia.

Amnesia?

Amnesia?

He doesn't even *remember* the explosion, he doesn't remember a *lot* of things.

He told the agents in charge of him that he doesn't even remember what they were working on when the accident happened.

He's very confused and manic. He has killed a number of people.

Get outta town.

Agents and civilians, and we are assuming that this visit here means you might be next.

Do you know why?

I honestly don't-- I--

SCREEEOOO

SCREEEOOOEEE

Are you people outta your mind?

I'm sorry, sir. We have orders.

Electro. Yes, sir.

You--well, you sold him to Wilson Fisk.

I think he's back in prison now.

Oy-- yoy yoy.

Wilson Fisk. Wilson Fisk.

Why'd I do that again?

The construction contracts for the dome.

Well, that was money well spent.

Well, what about the Sandman project? That's costing a small fortune.

Yes, and it's going fine, but as you can see we are having a couple of bumps in the road.

Timmy, feed the 56S to Hammer 1.

FEED: SATELLITE 45-11 DOCTOR JOHN SKRTIC
HAMMER RESEARCH FACILITY--FOURTH FLOOR TIME: 2:55 PM

FEED: SATELLITE 45-11 SANDMAN PROJECT. FLINT MARKO.
HAMMER INDUSTRIES RESEARCH FACILITY - SUBBASEMENT 2 TIME: 2:56 PM

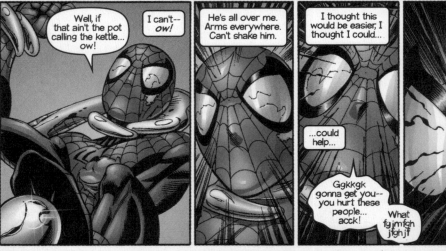

SMASH

Captain,
we have him
over here!

Is he
awake?

Over
here...

Take
off his
mask.

Mmmwhat's
goin' on?

He's
awake.

He's
up.

Lieutenant,
over here!!

Stay down!
Stay down!!

Don't
you move!

Don't you
move a muscle
or I will blow
your head
off!!

W-what?
What's goin'
on? Hey!

Psyche!

Aah! What is this?

THWIPP

THWIPP

Thank god my web shooters are still working.

Oh man, I'm gonna heave! Total head spins.

SSFOOOM

SSFOOOM

BLAM

BLAM

BLAM

SSFOOOM

BLAM
BLAM

What?
fg jm fgh jfgh jfgh jf

Guh
guh Nnguh
guh

Guh
guh Nnguh
guh

Guh
guh Nnguh
guh

Guh
Guh

Guh

Guh

Guh

Yes, of course--
but we have
confirmed that
the nuclear
facility is intact.

As promised
by our team of
experts--the
nuclear core
could, in fact,
withstand
any duress.

You know-- I was this close to being Spider-Man.

How many times do I have to hear that?

That's the price you pay for all of this.

You'll help me with this?

I'm, like, the Betsy Ross of super heroes. Was it Betsy Ross?

Yes.

Okay then...

...and maybe, you know, we'll do some more of that...other stuff we were just doing.

You sure you have to go?

Yeah-- --I think so.

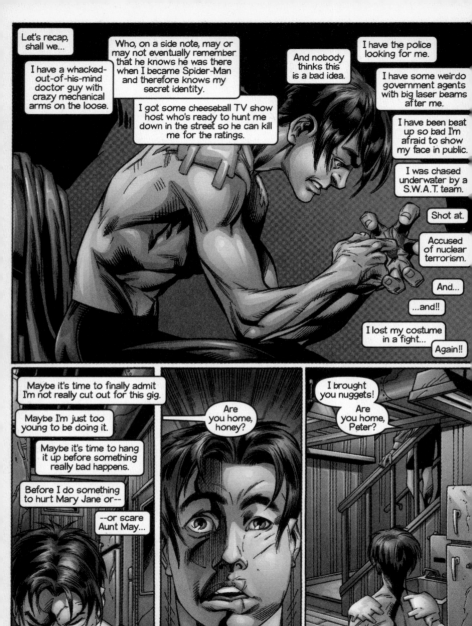

Whadaya think?

Hey, look at that.

Try it on.

Wow.

Man, I don't know what I would have done without you.

You don't have super sewing powers?

I don't even have the power not to lose my costume in the middle of a fight.

So, hey-- uh-- Do you, like, like that Gwen girl?

Uh-- --she's all right.

Kind of screwy, don't you think?

...Yeah.

But, hey, she's a lot more interesting than everyone else we know. Gotta give her that.

True.

Ta Daaa...

What? Are you leaving? Wh-where are you going all of a sudden?

Wow.

You are exactly what they refer to when they say "some piece of work."

Well, it was worth a shot.

I thought you handled that quite well, sir.

Be quiet.

BOOP

Justin Hammer.

Yes, he's right here.

What?

It's Doctor Skrtic again. He says it's very important.

Was I too subtle with him in the elevator?

Put it on the screen.

FEED SATELLITE 49-11 DR SKRTIC
HAMMER IND MED FACILITIES

Are you tryin' to be the focal point of all my rage, Doctah?

Because if so, it's working.

HAMMER IND.

There's no one at the check gate, sir?

Just-- just drive up...

Sir?

He gets nothing if he kills me.

Nothing if he kills me.

What is that?

Oh no...

And here we are--the hunt is almost over.

We have just received word from our local affiliate here in New York City that *Spider-Man*--Kraven the Hunter's elusive prey--has been spotted in the wilds of New Jersey.

He was last seen riding on top of a limousine down the Jersey turnpike.

The unidentified limo has reportedly pulled into a factory owned by famous enterpreneur Justin Hammer--

--where a rather odd bloke named Otto Octavius, who has been in the headlines for the last couple of days, has called an impromptu press conference of some kind.

Okay, you ready?

Hold on...yeah.

Aaaand... action!

We don't know the story behind this Octavius fellow yet-- but as this is a pre-taped broadcast and as the press conference is going on even as we speak...

...by the time you see this broadcast all should be made clear to all of us about just what--

cut!

See, this is why I didn't want to do this now!

What?

You're improvising and you aren't making any sense.

Just say -- we found Spider-Man and we're on our way to him.

Then we pan over -- we show a shot of Kraven meditating and that's it.

Okay, okay.

The rest is just gibber gabber.

Aaaand... action!

As you can see the entire crew of the Kraven the Hunter show has packed itself onto the Kraven American tour bus.

As regular viewers know-- Kraven's prehunt meditation ritual is the single most important part of the hunt.

But with the complexity of modern society and the opportunity afforded us by this oh-so-rare Spider-Man sighting...

...Kraven will forgo the hunt and instead face his prey head on. Head to head. In front of the world press.

I am whispering to give Kraven all due respect as he focuses his spirits on his ancient ritual meditation.

But just what kind of battle awaits Kraven?

This American Spider-Man is an unknown entity -- a foe beyond anything he has ever faced before.

Aaand... cut.

Can I do it again?

No.

I think I can do it better.

We got it. Do we got it?

We got it.

Kraven, you okay, Krave baby?

Yes.

We're almost there, baby.

Almost time for television history.

SCREEEEEEEEEEEEE

Coward...

Oh, my...

SMACK SHK

Aaaaiiieeee!!

Aagghh!!

Man, my instincts stink!

My instincts stink just about as much as your *haircut!*

See, the thing is-- I still kinda feel bad for you and your silly arms incident...

...so, I'm all like: maybe he just needs a hug?

Aaii!!

CRASH!

Hold back and see what's what.

BZZT

CLICK

And the one time I remember to do all this and you're acting all like Dennis Hopper in any of his early to mid-nineties movie roles.

BAM
BAM

SPING

PING

KINK
KINK
KINK

You okay? Are you hit?

Shh--I'm filming.

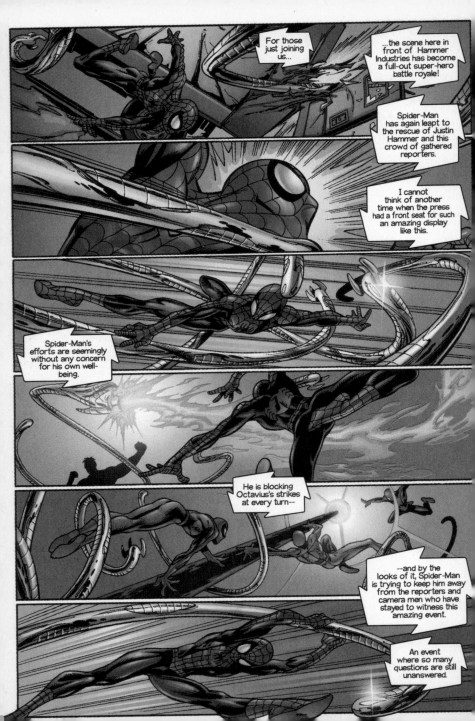

So--uh--hey, ugrrhh--where'd--uh all--these little new gadgets and doodads come from?

The Sharper Image catalogue for megalomaniacs?

These are new adjustments, adjustments *I* made.

ZTTTT

I am my *own* creation! I am in control of my *own* destiny!

Good for you-- I, on the other hand, am barely in control of my own bladder at this point.

Grrrr!!!

WSR

Did you get that?

You're a coward, Hammer! Hiding behind your little freaks.

It's time to show these people what you are!

Oh no ho ono ho on

Who's the monster now, Hammer? Who's the monster now??

Our time has come, insect. Our battle is now.

Uh-huh. Whatever.

Actually why don't you and your little buddies help me get this girl out of the car because I think she's in shock or something.

Are you okay? Is he okay?

I -- I think he's dead.

Oh man...

I think he had a heart attack. He's -- he's dead!!

Hey, listen, I'm going to rip the door off. Can you grab the girl? But try not to--

--uh, what are you doing?

We will do battle!

No, we won't.

Are you kidding me?

HUYRRAGGH!

HUYRRAGGH!

WHUUUFFF

Seriously, stop it!

Man, I am *not* in the mood for this.

HUYRRAGGH!

Dude, cut it *out*.

HUYRRAGGH!

HUYRRAGGH!

Hey, what is *wrong* with you?

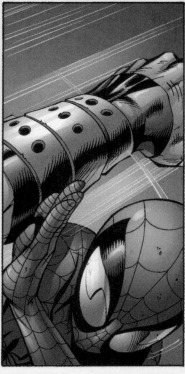

Thank you-- thank you for saving me.

It's-- uh--

Thank you...

It's okay. It's okay.

Tell me you got it.

Ssshhh...

CLAP

CLAP CLAP

CLAP

CLAP CLAP CLAP

CLAP

CLAP CLAP

CLAP CLAP CLAP

CLAP CLAP CLAP CLAP CLAP CLAP CLAP

Uh -- okay. Yeah -- uh -- thanks.

That -- that was amazing.

Did you know Justin Hammer?

No.

Anybody headed back towards Manhattan? I kinda need a ride.

Uh -- not really, two people died.

But he trashed you in the press -- he tried to blame you for all this --

Well, yeah -- but that has nothing to do with this. It's sad when someone dies for no good reason like that.

How's *that* for a home run?

Oh -- uh -- we're still on the air?

Well, there you have it, Tom. A world exclusive interview with the triumphant Spider-Man.

And let me say from this perspective it seems that many of us have *misjudged* him from the getgo.

It looks like New York has a true hero in our midst.

Tom, I don't know if you can see this, but there's some kind of commotion over at the Kraven the Hunter tour bus.

It looks like the police have stopped the Kraven camp from trying to flee the scene.

It would seem that the police plan on arresting Kraven and his crew for their behavior here tonight.

Hold on, it seems we have even more new arrivals to this tumultuous scene.

This is Carter. We have a big fat P.D.A.

We need a doggie bag, asap.

Agent Woo, make sure the Hammer building is secure.

We're going to clear the civilians and pick up the Doctor.

Seriously? Wow. Yeah -- I -- I was waiting on a train and --

Where were you?

At the -- you know -- at the Daily Bugle.

Really? Because I called over there and they said you hadn't come in all week.

What?

Where were you?

No -- I -- was there -- 'course I was there.

They -- they're all kinds of people down at the Bugle. They all don't know me.

They -- a lot of people think I'm just "The Kid."

They probably had me mistaken with somebody else. Yeah...

Is this a bruise?

That's right! No more Bugle!

What?

No more Mary Jane giggle-thons in the base-ment.

You go to school and you come home from school.

A straight beeline to and from.

And I will be calling your principal and your job to inform them of this as well.

Come on!

Yeah? "Come on?"

And if you can't figure out how to do this --

-- I will call the cops on you myself! Is that understood?!

Yes, ma'am.

Now get out of my sight until you can figure out how to tell the truth.

SLAM!

...are we back on the -- okay. Uh, if you can hear me, Tom...

This was an amazing night here at Hammer Industries. Justin Hammer dead of a heart attack at age sixty-seven.

Spider-Man selflessly battling odds obviously not in his favor against both Otto Octavius and syndicated television personality Kraven the Hunter.

Kraven the Hunter is under arrest. Otto Octavius in government custody.

And Spider-Man giving the press the first look into what makes him tick.

We'll be staying with this story until we get more answers as to what events shaped this fateful night in the...

Finally... big time super hero...

...and I'm grounded.